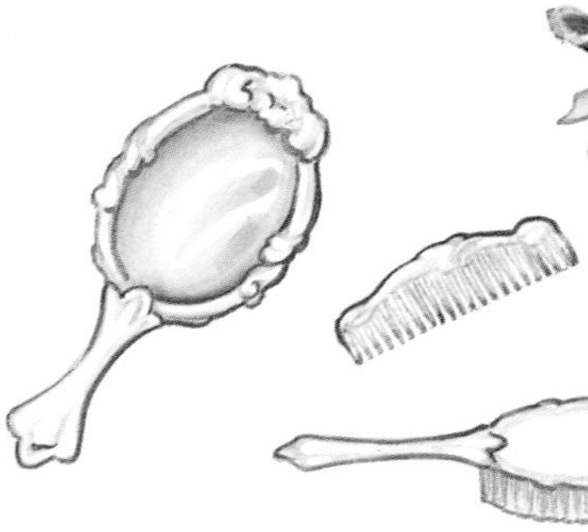

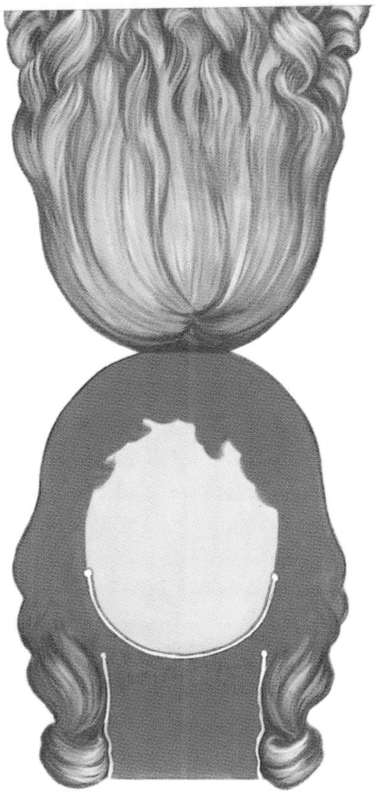

Aimee's
Accessories

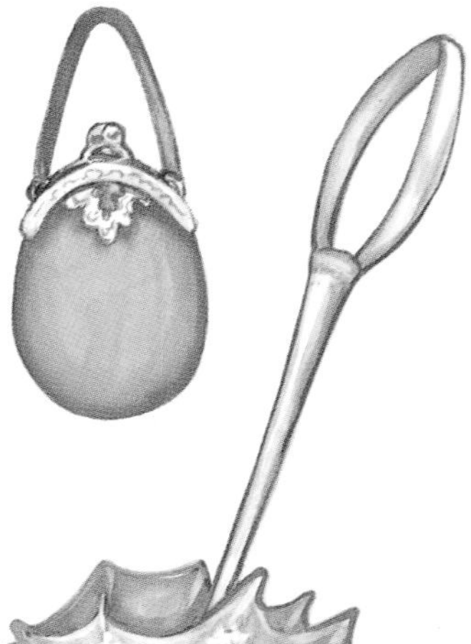

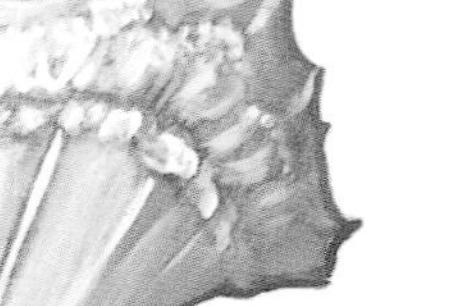

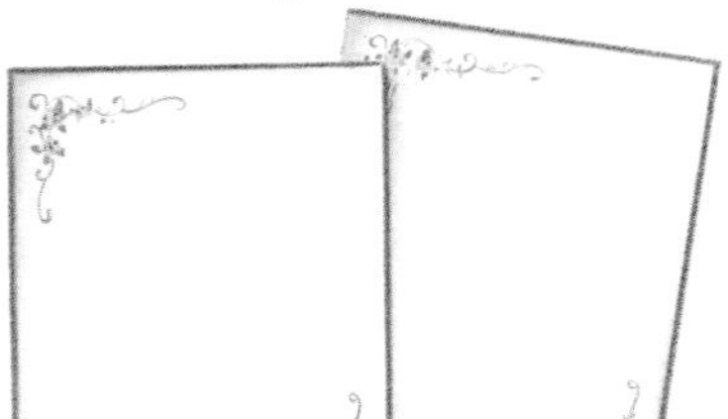

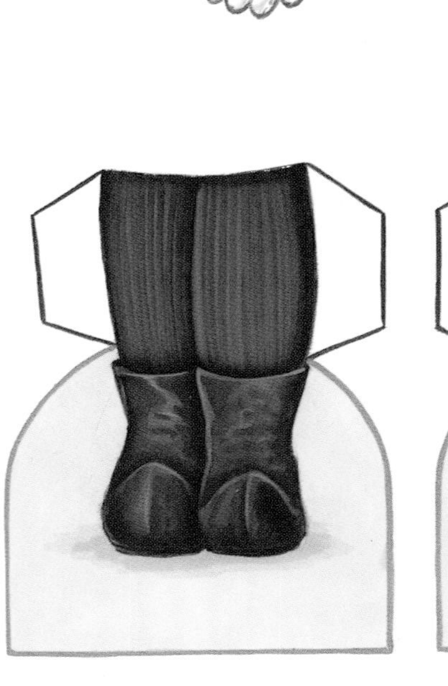

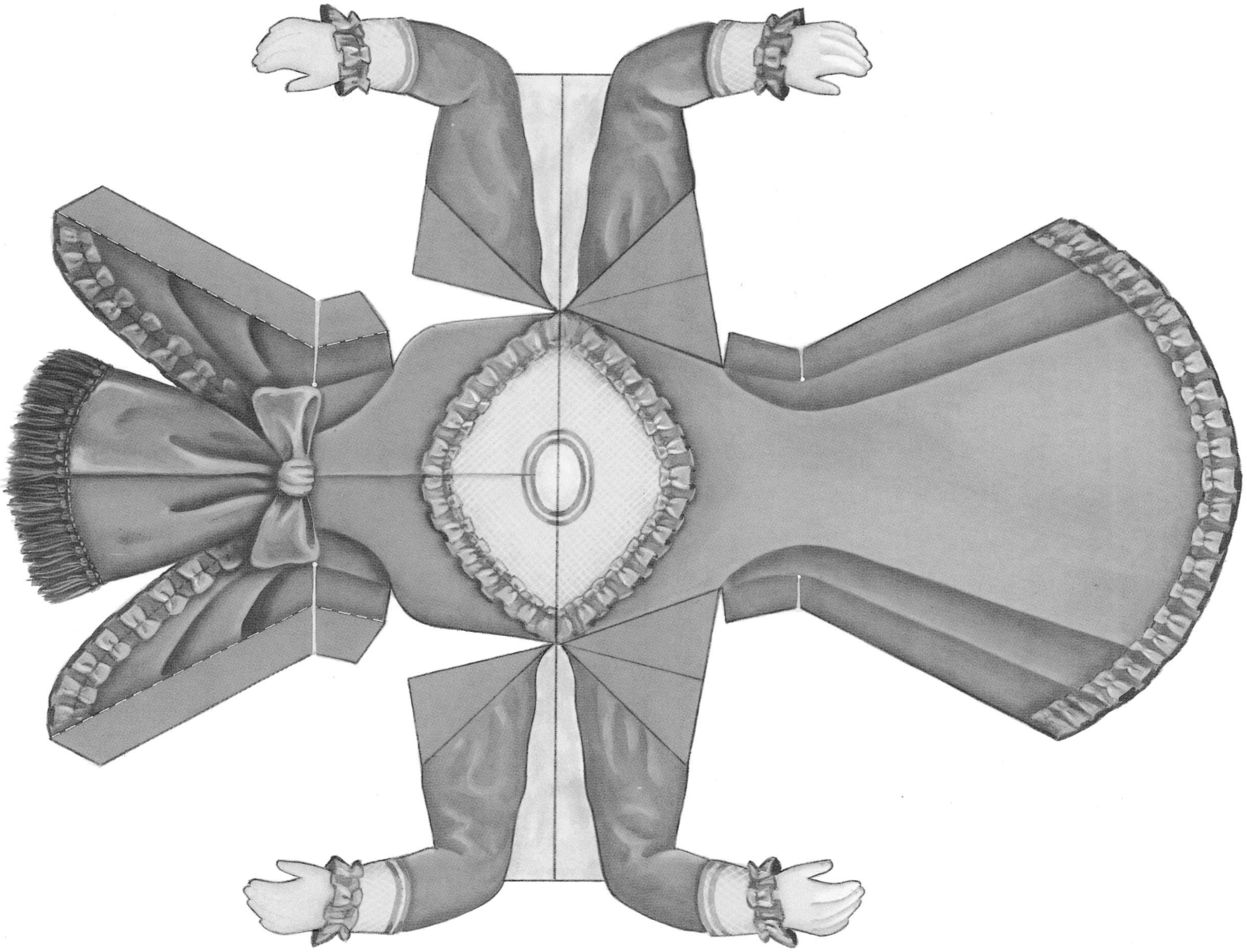

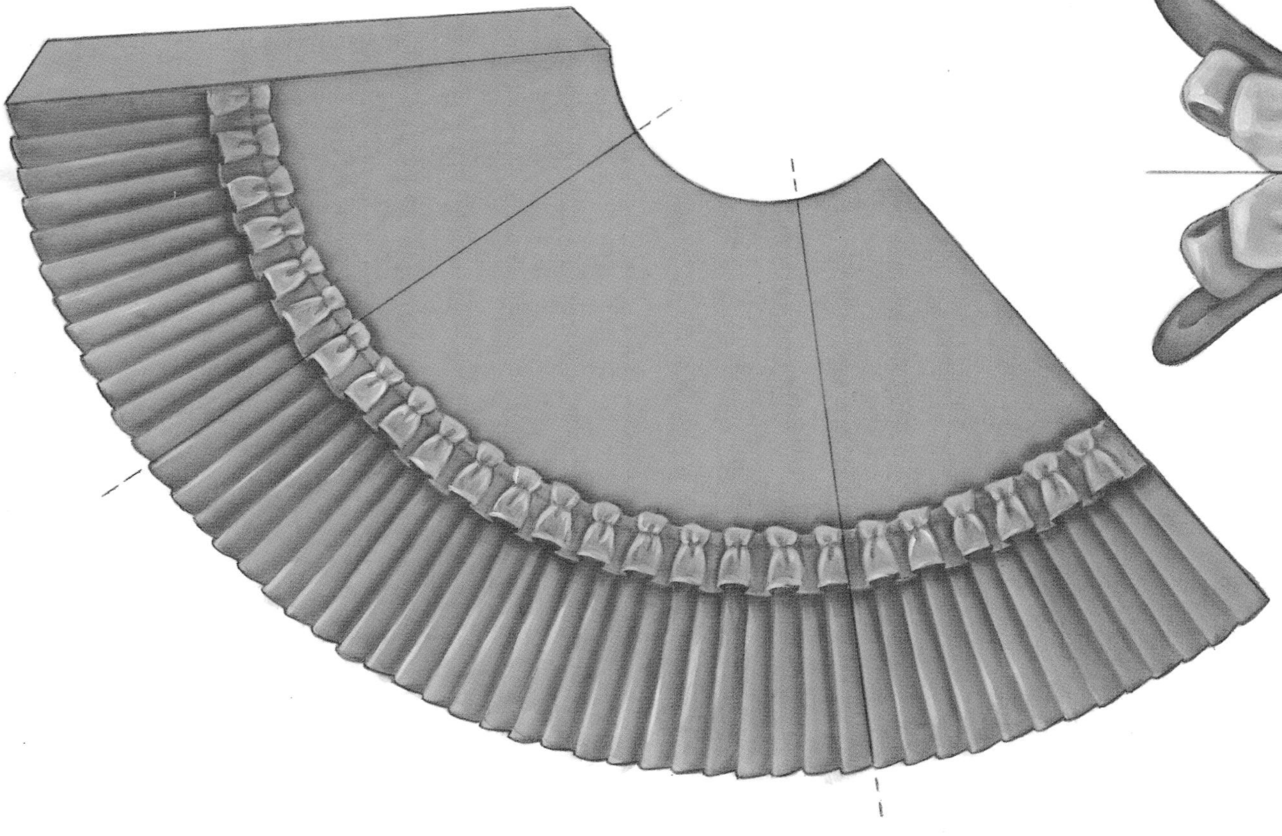

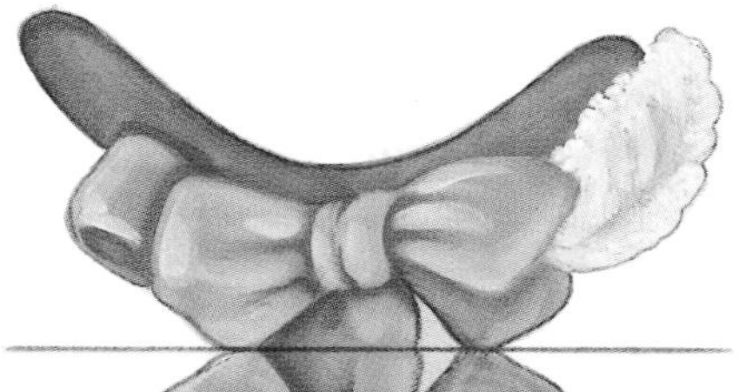

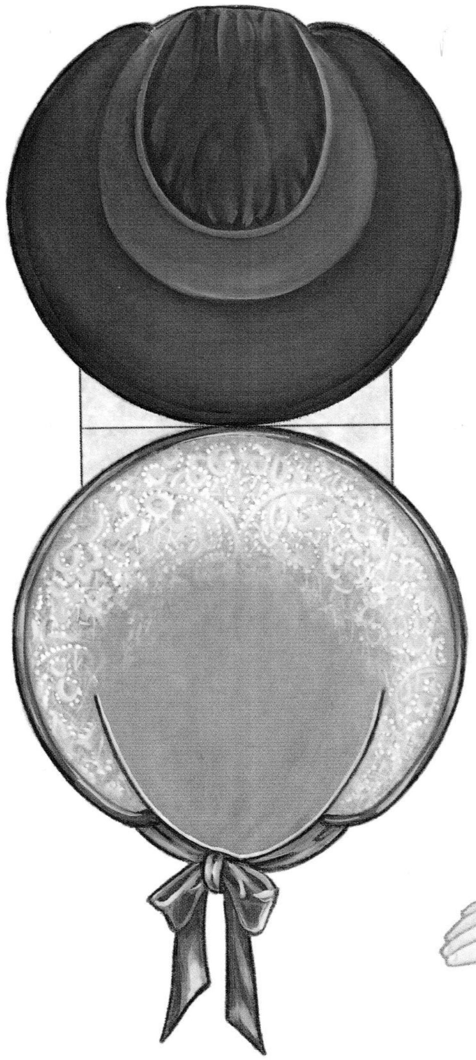
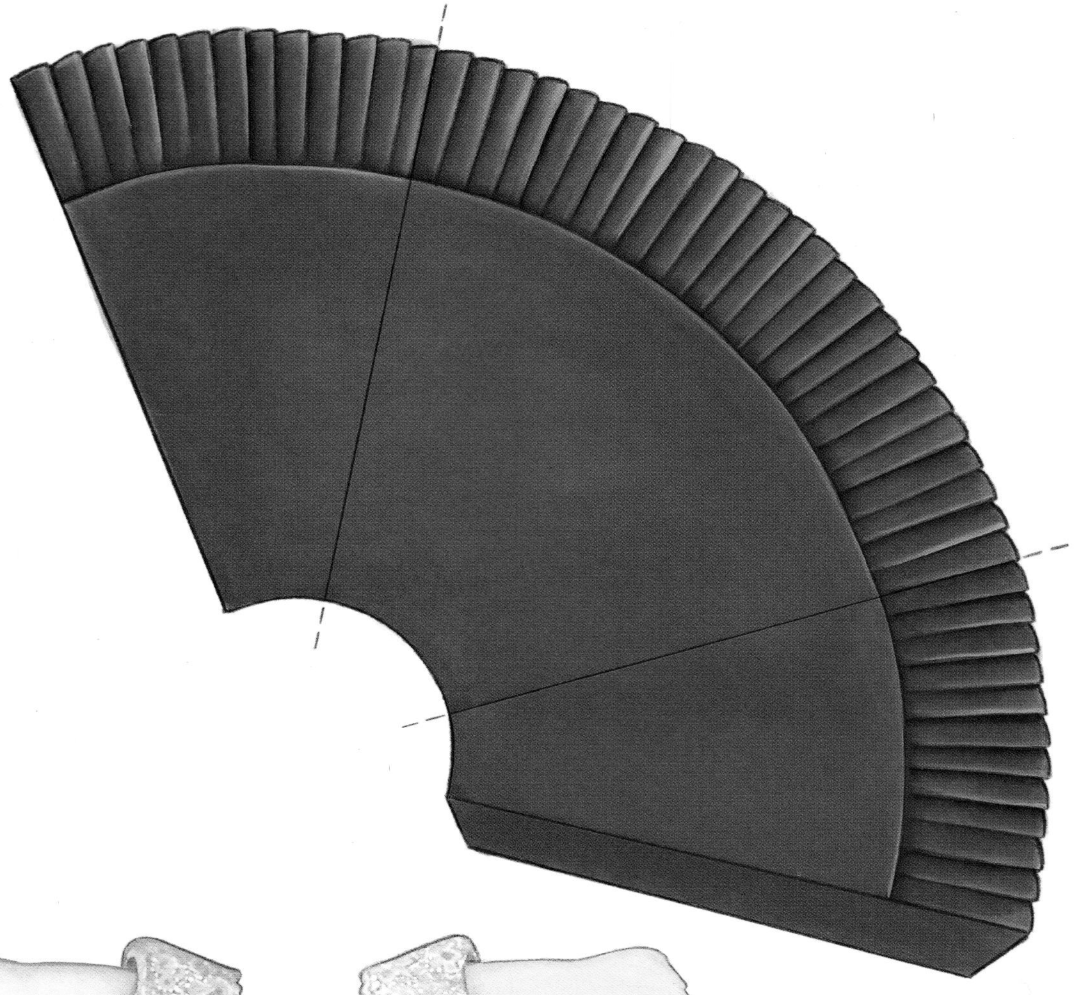
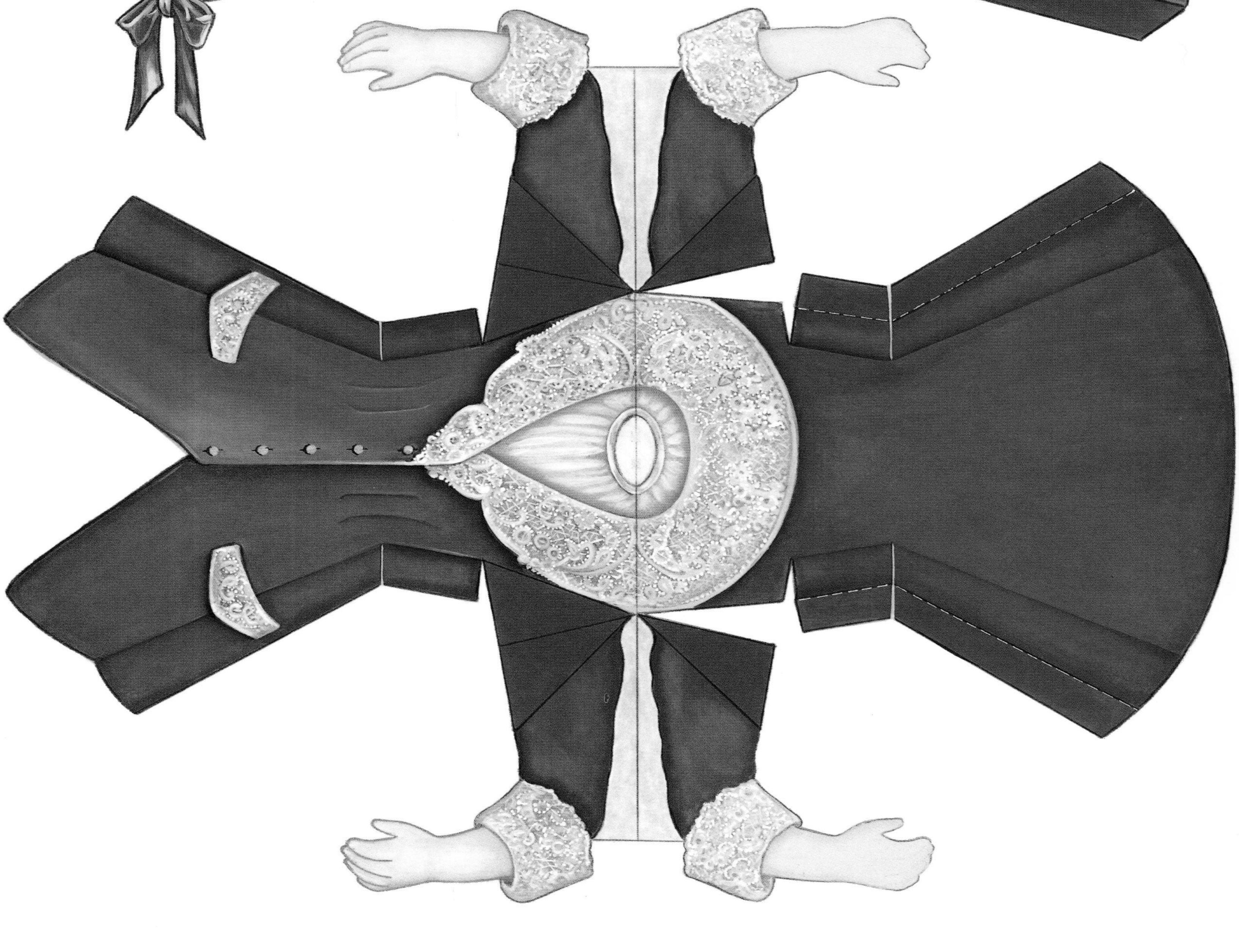

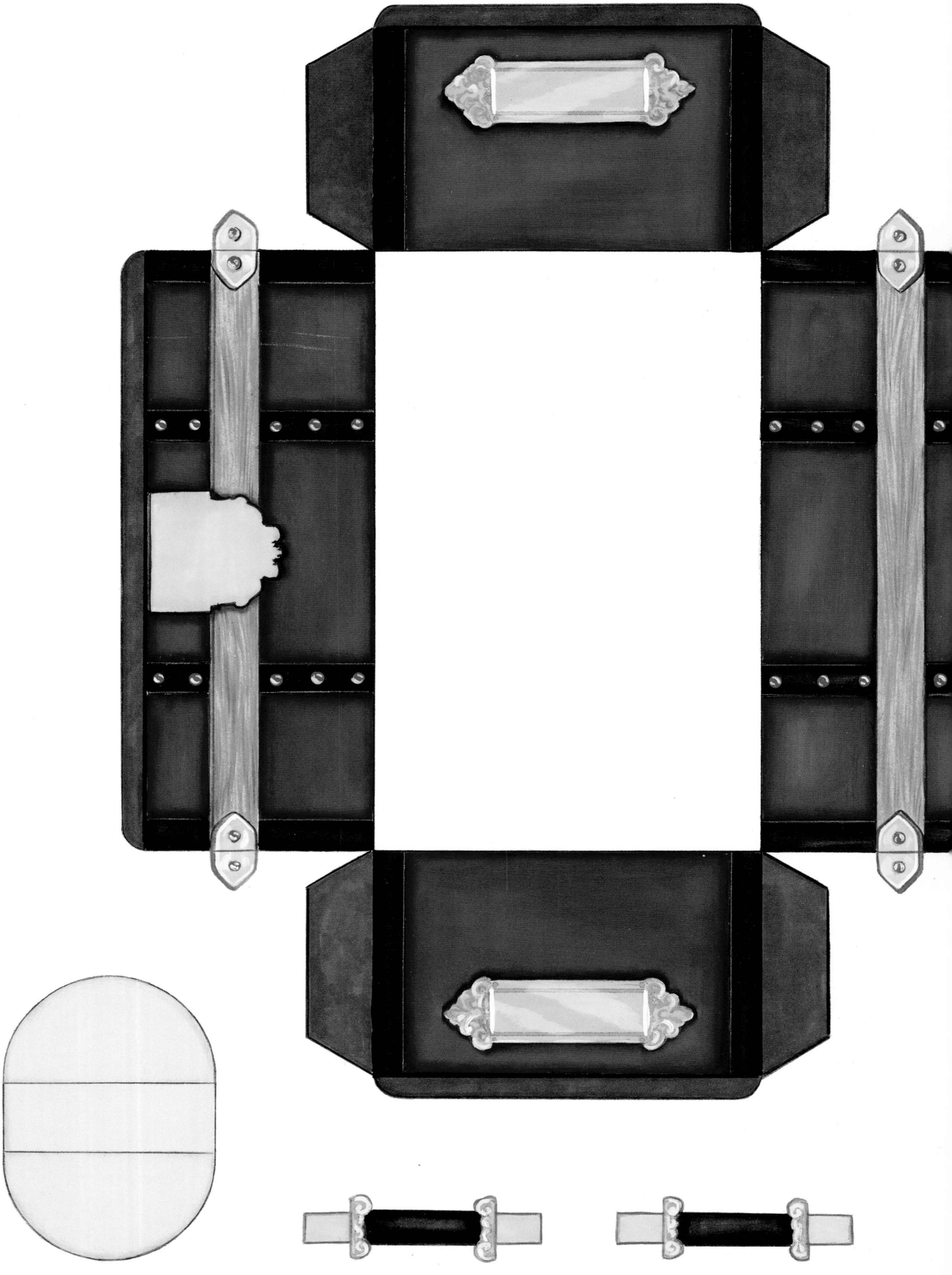

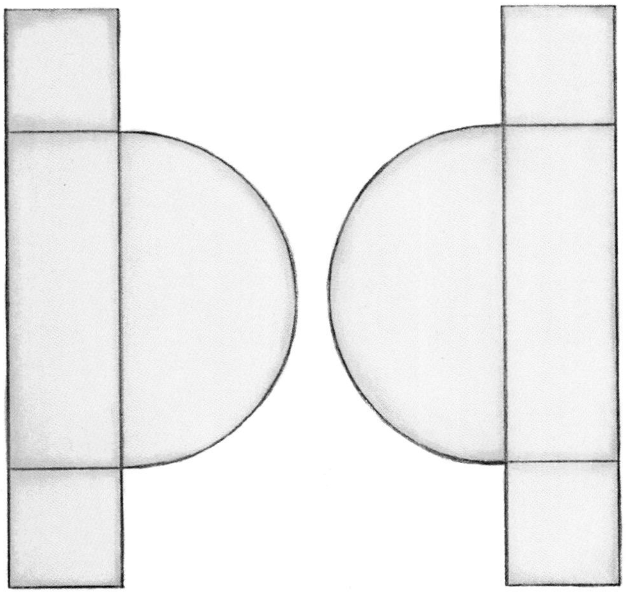

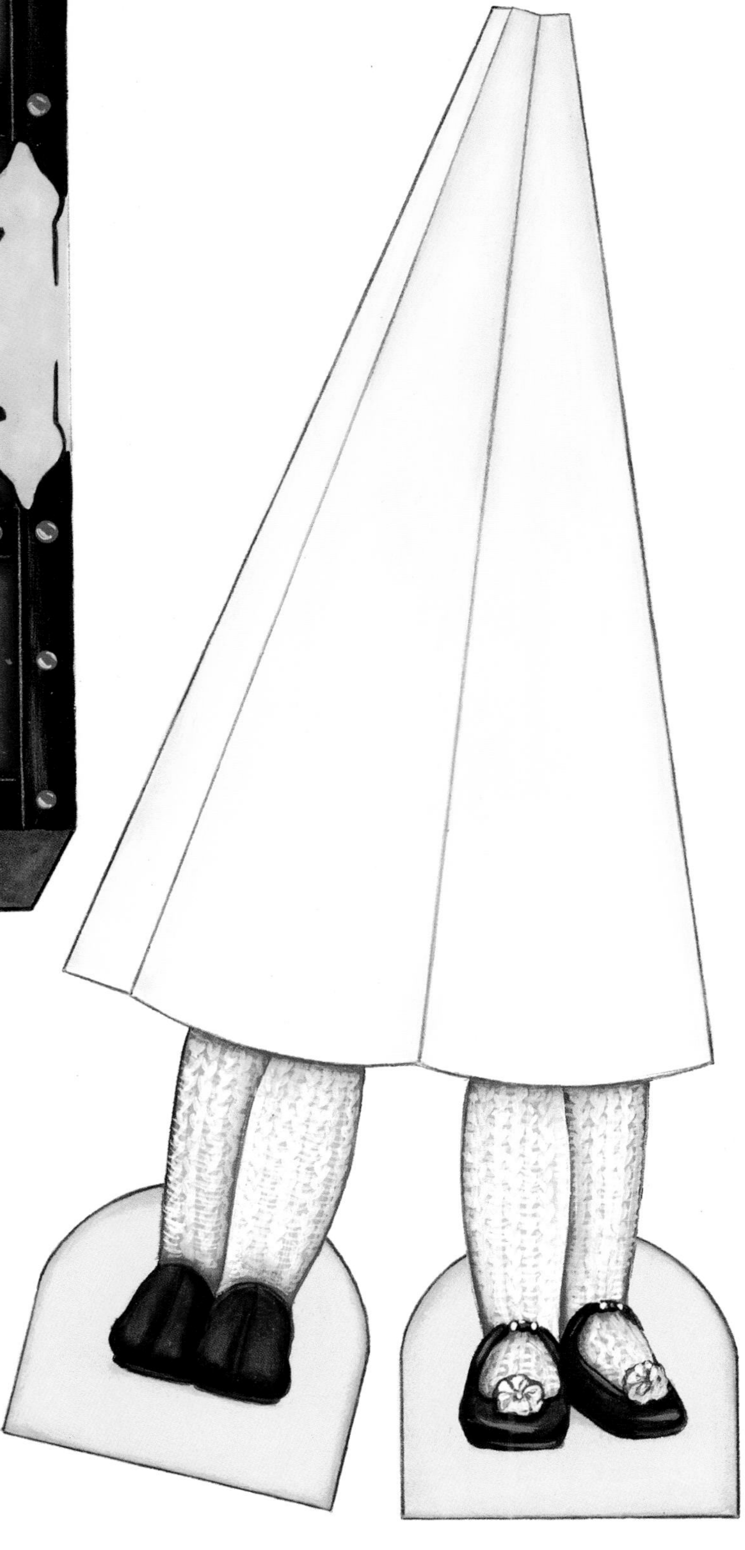

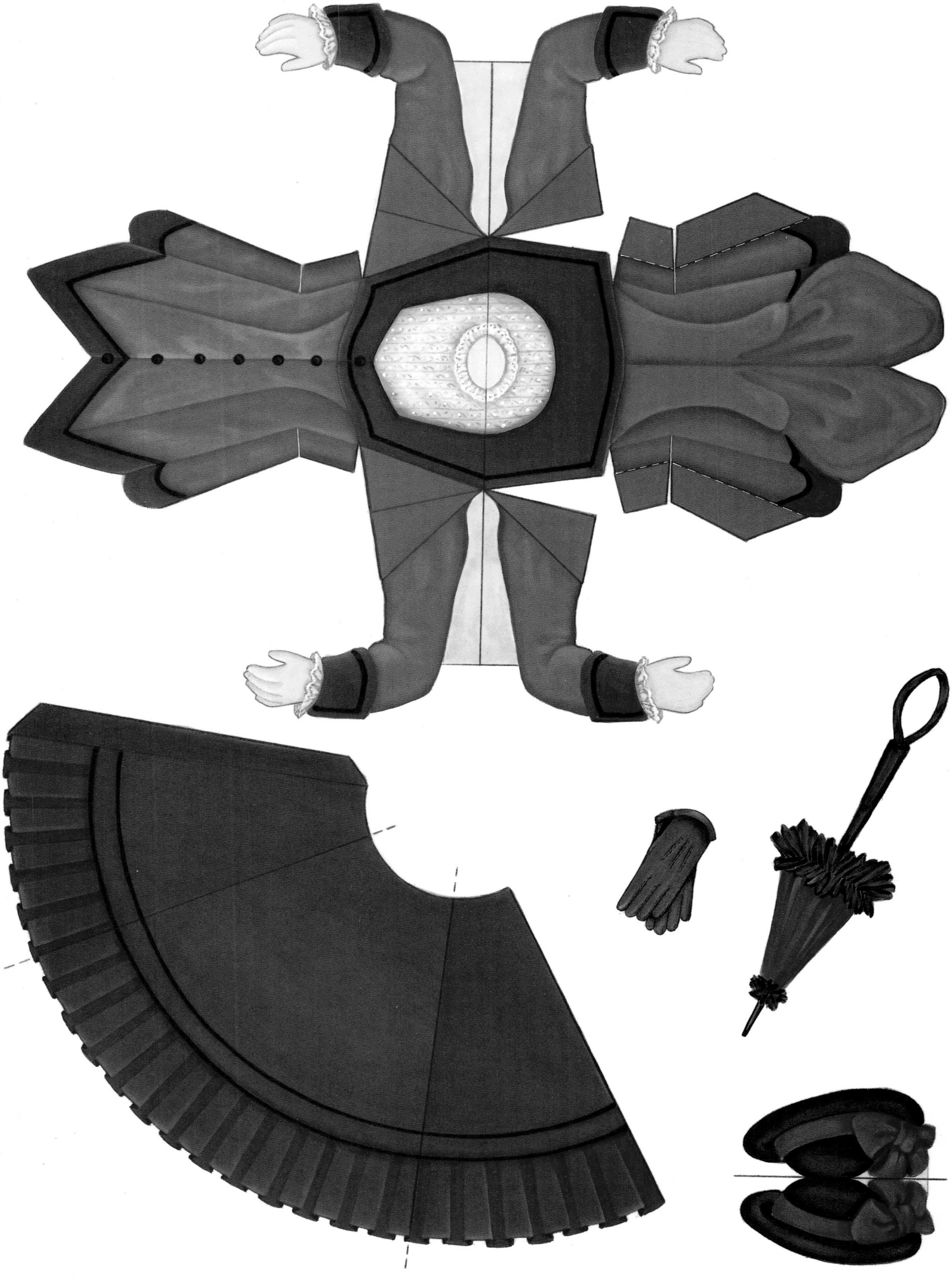

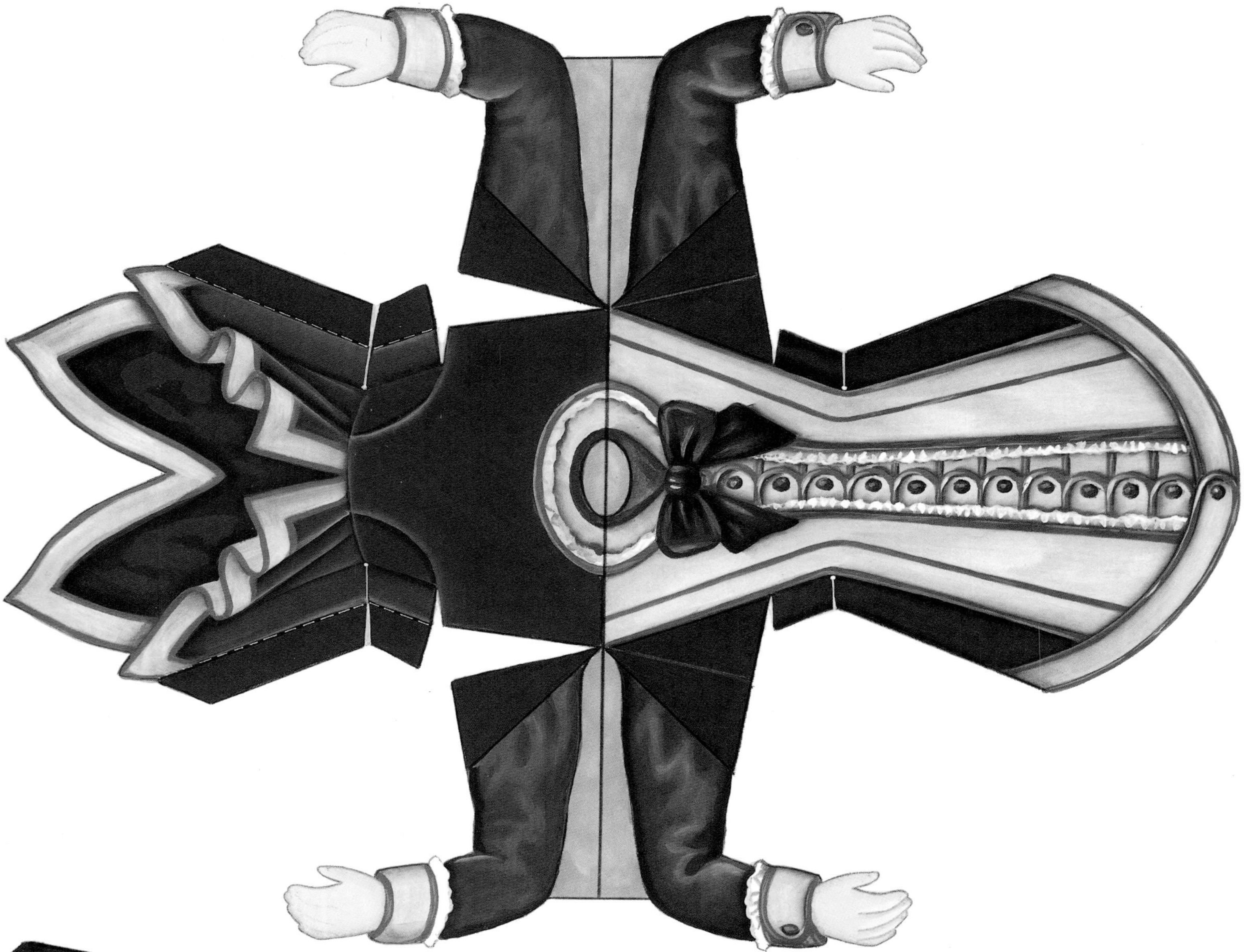
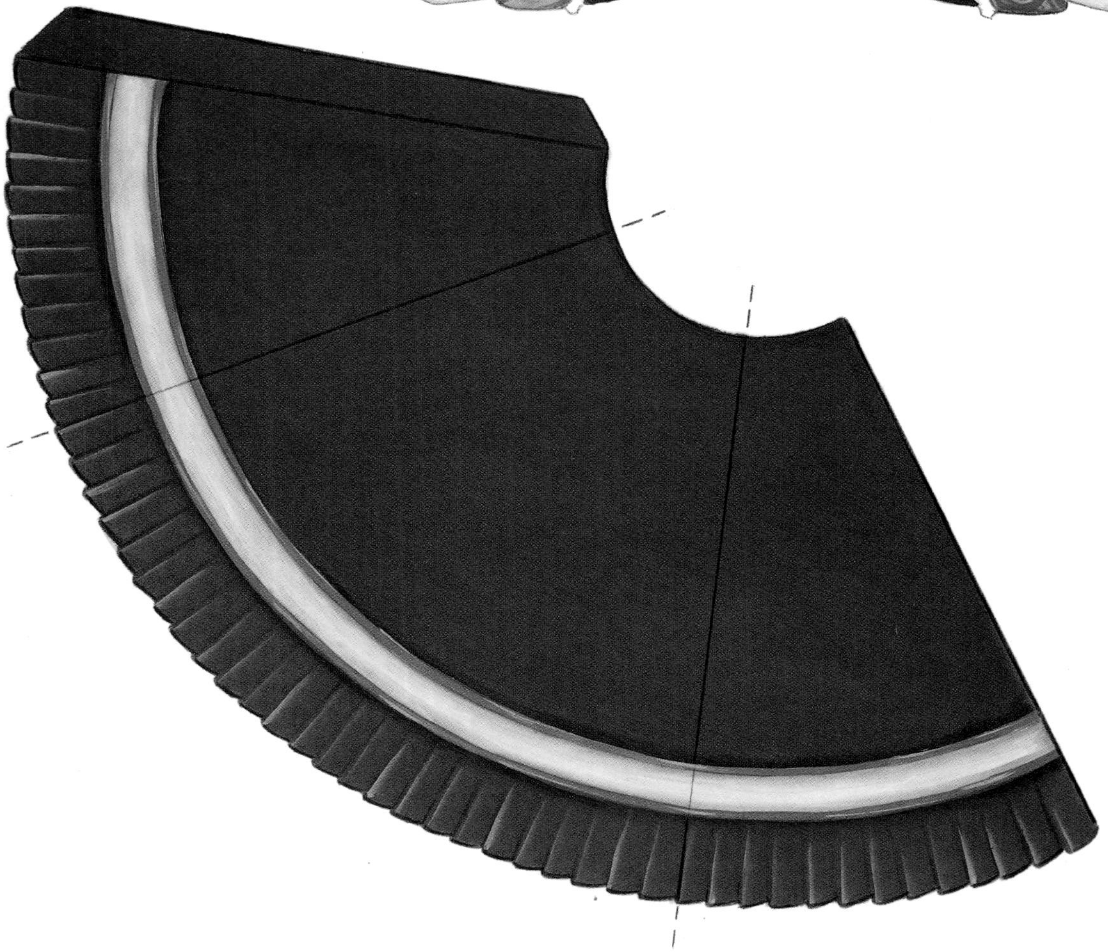